9.95
JH4664

FUNCTIONAL BASIC READING SERIES

About King

by

Al Tudyman
Director of Special Education
Oakland, California, Public Schools

and

Marvin C. Groelle
Supervisor of Classes
for the Mentally Retarded
Oakland, California, Public Schools

STANWIX HOUSE, INC.
PITTSBURGH, PENNSYLVANIA

FUNCTIONAL BASIC READING SERIES

Copyright, 1963, by Stanwix House, Incorporated
Pittsburgh, Pennsylvania 15204
All rights reserved.
International rights reserved.
Printed in the United States of America

Published simultaneously in Canada by
J. M. Dent & Sons (Canada) Ltd.
Toronto, Ontario

ISBN 0-87076-015-7

Library of Congress Catalog Card Number: 62-21470

Stories

�֎ ✖ ✖

King

King

King

King

King

King

Bill

Bill

Bill

Bill

Bill

Bill

King and Bill

Bill and King

King and Bill

Bill and King

King and Bill

Bill and King

King and Mary

Bill, King, and Mary

Mary

King and Mary

Bill, King, and Mary

Bill, Mary, and King

King, Bill, and Mary

Bill, King, and Mary

Mary, King, and Bill

Bill, King, and Mary

Run, King

Run, King.

Run, King, run.

Bill and Mary run.

Mary, Bill, and King run.

Run, Mary and Bill.

Run to Mary and Bill

Run, King. Run to Mary.

Run, King. Run to Bill.

Run, King. Run, run.

Run, King. Run to Mary.

Run, King. Run, Bill.
Run to Mary.

Run, King.
Run to Mary. Run to Mary.

Run, King. Run, run.
Run to Mary.

Run, King. Run, run.
Run, Bill. Run to Mary.

Run, King. Run to Mary.
King and Bill run.

Bill and King Jump

Run, King.
Run to Bill and Mary.

Jump, Bill.
Run and jump.

Run and jump, King.
Jump to Bill.

Jump, King, jump.
Run and jump.

Jump, Bill.
Jump to King.

Run, King, run.
Run to Bill.

Run, Mary.
Run to Bill and King.

King

Run, King.
Jump and run.

Jump, King, jump.
Mary and Bill run to King.

Bill and Mary jump.
Run, King. Run, run.

Run, run, King.
Run to Mary.

Run and jump, King.
Bill and Mary run to King.

Facts About This Book

ABOUT KING is the first of six texts written for Level II of *Functional Basic Reading,* a series of readers and supplementary aids designed to meet the developmental and remedial reading needs of children whose chronological and social ages are significantly above their reading ages. A big book which duplicates the first two stories from ABOUT KING will precede the introduction of this textbook. ABOUT KING A-2 will be most effectively used by the pupil whose approximate age characteristics are: chronological age—eight years to nine years; social age—seven years to eight years; mental age—five years, six months to five years, nine months.

Mary, Bill, and King, the principal characters in ABOUT KING, are members of the same family who appeared in the preceding readiness materials titled OUR DOG. Each story in ABOUT KING relates an experience that Mary and Bill have with their new pet.

Three of the eight "social life needs" which have been incorporated into *Functional Basic Reading* are relevant to these stories: learning to get along with others, learning the wise use of leisure time, and learning homemaking and simple money management.

Illustrations are found on every story page in the book to enrich the meanings and concepts found in the stories. Characters are illustrated in a social setting which is commensurate with the learning potential and aspiration of the children who read them.

ABOUT KING introduces four new words from the controlled vocabulary list* used in developing *Functional Basic Reading.* Each new word is repeated six times before another is introduced. The new words are repeated many more times throughout the book.

Provisions are made in the teacher guide BEGINNING FUNCTIONAL BASIC READING for the sequential and systematic development of a sight vocabulary and the ex-

---

*A. Tudyman and M.C. Groelle, *A Functional Basic Word List for Special Pupils* (Pittsburgh: Stanwix House, Inc., 1963).

periential background which is needed for learning the words and meanings presented in these stories.

Word List

The Word List which follows indicates the page on which each of the four new words is first introduced in ABOUT KING. The words printed in italic type are bonus words. Bonus words as used in this book are character names.

5. *King*	20. . . .	34. . . .	48. . . .
6. . . .	21. . . .	35. . . .	49. jump
7. . . .	22. . . .	36. . . .	50. . . .
8. . . .	23. *Mary*	37. . . .	51. . . .
9. . . .	24. . . .	38. . . .	52. . . .
10. . . .	25. . . .	39. to	53. . . .
11. *Bill*	26. . . .	40. . . .	54. . . .
12. . . .	27. . . .	41. . . .	55. . . .
13. . . .	28. . . .	42. . . .	56. . . .
14. . . .	29. . . .	43. . . .	57. . . .
15. . . .	30. . . .	44. . . .	58. . . .
16. . . .	31. . . .	45. . . .	59. . . .
17. and	32. . . .	46. . . .	60. . . .
18. . . .	33. run	47. . . .	61. . . .
19. . . .			62. . . .

Acknowledgments

Grateful acknowledgment is made to the following consultants who aided in the development of this text in the *Functional Basic Reading Series*.

Amy A. Allen,
>   *Assistant Professor, Department of Special Education, Ohio University*

Jack W. Birch,
>   *Associate Dean, School of Education, University of Pittsburgh*

Darrel J. Mase,
>   *Formerly Dean, College of Health Related Professions, University of Florida*

Al Tudyman,
>   *Director, Special Education, Oakland (California) Public Schools*

Martha G. Weber,
>   *Formerly Director, Reading Center, Bowling Green (Ohio) State University*